ER DAY...

Ciára Walsh

Balls bounce,
Hands clap!
Skipping ropes,
Slap, slap!
Hand stands
By the wall,
Willie Wilson
Best of all!

Shouts and
laughter,
Big din!
Whistle goes!
All in!

PEEP

SCHOOL

£3.40

Bunty FOR GIRLS

Contents

PICTURE STORIES

Pg.	
6	THE GREAT ESCAPE
17	SISTER SUZIE
26	PINKIE
36	ROBINA HOOD
49	THE COMP
58	A SADDLE FOR STRAWBERRY
65	THE PAINTING
81	THE FOUR MARYS
92	THE GOOD FAIRY
97	THE K.O. KIDS
113	BRASSRIBS

PHOTO STORIES

Pg.	
39	SECOND FIDDLE SARAH
109	DEAR KATY . . .

FEATURES ETC.

Pg.	
16, 125	BUNTY, A GIRL LIKE YOU!
25	HAGGIS
33	THE STATUE OF LIBERTY IS IN — DENMARK??
46	WHO IS SYLVIE?
48	DESIGN A FASHION
78	LEADING LADIES
80	WHATEVER NECKST?
91	TOOTS
121	BUNTY ANNUAL CALENDAR

Printed and Published
in Great Britain by
D. C. THOMSON & CO., LTD.,
185 Fleet Street,
London EC4A 2HS.
© D. C. THOMSON & CO., LTD., 1990.
ISBN 0-85116-470-6

THE GREAT ESCAPE

PAT PERKINS loved her part-time holiday job at a small wildlife park — until one evening at closing time . . .

GO AWAY, LEO! I'M NOT YOUR SUPPER!

HE'S USUALLY QUITE TAME. I'LL RISK A RUN FOR THE GATE.

I FORGOT ALL THESE GATES ARE LOCKED BY ELECTRONIC GADGETS OVERNIGHT.

PULL HANDLE IN EMERGENCY ONLY !

Barney Brayne was Pat's cousin and assistant manager . . .

NOW ELLA THE ELEPHANT! OH, WHAT SHALL WE DO, BARNEY?

FIRST NOTIFY ALL THE LOCAL AUTHORITIES.

But just outside.

HEE-HOO.

LINE'S GONE DEAD. I'LL TRY TO DRIVE THE PICK-UP TRUCK INTO TOWN BEFORE ANY OF OUR ANIMALS GET THERE.

THIS WOULD HAPPEN JUST WHEN I'D BEEN LEFT IN CHARGE WITH ONLY PART-TIME HELPERS LIKE YOU! IT COULD MEAN OUR ZOO BEING FORCED TO CLOSE!

LOOK! THERE'S JIMMY!

I'LL USE THE CATCHING POLE.

NEVER MIND THE GIRAFFE! JUST LOOK WHAT THOSE CHIMPS ARE DOING TO MY COTTAGE ROOF!

10

Some minutes later . . .

MIDCLAYS BANK LTD

THAT'S GEORGE, OUR GORILLA! HE MUST HAVE CAUSED THAT ALARM ABOUT A BANK ROBBERY!

HE MAY HAVE GOT TIRED AND THOUGHT THIS WAS A WAY BACK INTO HIS COSY SLEEPING CAGE.

Inside the bank . . .

I'LL SOON BURN THE LOCK OUT WITH THIS THERMAL LANCE.

YES — ER — BUT LOOK . . .

OH, BLIMEY! A GORILLA!

GRRR!

YEEAAH!

I SAW IT ALL! POOR GEORGE! DID THE NASTY MEN SINGE YOUR CHEST?

I GAVE THESE OFFICERS A LIFT IN OUR TRUCK.

JUST AS WELL! THERE REALLY WAS A ROBBERY GOING ON HERE!

JUST GETTING A REPORT OF A LION LOOSE IN COLONEL BAGHAM'S COUNTRY HOUSE GARDENS.

THAT'LL BE LEO! THE COLONEL'S GROUNDS BORDER OURS!

So, after getting the gorilla safely home . . .

WE MUST GET LEO WITH OUR TRANQUILLISER DART GUN BEFORE THE COLONEL SHOOTS HIM FOR REAL!

NO NEED FOR PANIC! SOON BAG THE BEAST WITH MY OLD HUNTING GUN!

LEO MUST BE IN THOSE BUSHES!

HE COULD END UP AS A LION SKIN IN COLONEL BAGHAM'S STATELY HOME!

HOW EXCITING!

LET'S FILM IT ALL!

Finally . . .

GOT HIM AT LAST!

PHEW! YOU'RE A ROTTEN SHOT, BARNEY! SOME OF THOSE SLEEP DARTS NEARLY HIT ME!

NOW WE HAVE TO GET LEO INTO OUR TRUCK.

WE'LL HELP.

Next morning, outside the zoo office . . .

WHAT DO THEY WANT?

DAMAGES! FOR ALL THE MISCHIEF OUR ANIMALS CAUSED!

ER — ABOUT THAT POLICE CAR, INSPECTOR . . .

NEVER MIND THAT! YOUR GORILLA HELPED US TO CAPTURE THOSE TWO BANK-ROBBERS.

AS MANAGER OF THAT BANK I AM ARRANGING FOR YOU AND YOUR ZOO TO RECEIVE A GOOD MONEY REWARD.

14

Bunty A GIRL LIKE YOU

GREAT! IT'S BEEN SNOWING!

YOU'RE NOT GOING OUT, ARE YOU? YOUR LITTLE COUSINS ARE COMING OVER TO VISIT.

I WON'T BE LONG, MUM.

WHEE! THIS IS GREAT FUN. I'LL POP ROUND TO LISA'S AND SEE IF SHE AND JO WANT TO COME OUT.

WE WERE PLAYING RECORDS, BUNTY. IT'S FAR TOO COLD TO COME OUT.

OH, COME ON!

IT'S FREEZING.

IT'S NOT THAT BAD. COME ON, LET'S HAVE A SLIDE.

HA! HA! THIS IS GREAT!

HA-HA!

OUCH!

Later—

BUNTY, YOUR LITTLE COUSINS ARE HERE.

HI, BUNTY. COMING TO HELP US BUILD A SNOWMAN?

OOH! I HATE WINTER!

Petra broke the news to Mum.

WELL, ALL RIGHT — I SUPPOSE WE OWE IT TO YOUR UNCLE. HE'S BEEN VERY GOOD TO US SINCE YOUR DAD DIED.

OH, THIS IS REALLY TOO BAD OF YOUR UNCLE. WE'LL JUST HAVE TO TELL HIM THAT WE CAN'T MANAGE TWO CHIMPS.

BUT WHAT WILL UNCLE JIM DO WITH POOR LITTLE JESS? SHE'S SO SMALL AND NERVOUS. I DON'T THINK SHE WOULD ENJOY BEING KEPT AT THE ZOO UNTIL HER OWNER GETS BETTER.

DON'T WORRY, MUM — WE'LL COPE.

But Jess was very different from friendly Suzie.

POOR JESS — SHE'S SCARED. SHE WON'T COME OUT FROM BEHIND THE SOFA.

WHAT SHE NEEDS IS SOME TIME TO HERSELF TO SETTLE IN. COME ON, EVERYONE, LET'S LEAVE HER ALONE FOR A WHILE.

But, later —

JESS HAS DISAPPEARED. I CAN'T FIND HER ANYWHERE. GO AND FIND HER, SUZIE. LOOK FOR YOUR FRIEND.

OO! OO! OO!

SUZIE! STOP! JESS CAN HARDLY BE HIDING IN THE DRAWERS OR UNDER THE BEDCLOTHES.

WOW! WHAT A MESS!

SUZIE SEEMS TO THINK THAT JESS MIGHT HAVE GONE UPSTAIRS.

I ONLY HOPE THAT SHE HASN'T MANAGED TO GET OUT OF THE HOUSE.

Suzie began to search.

18

Then —

MUM, COME AND SEE — WE'VE FOUND JESS!

WHAT? WHERE IS SHE? IS SHE ALL RIGHT?

SHE'S ASLEEP ON TOP OF THE TWINS' TOY CUPBOARD, AND SHE'S CUDDLING ROBIN'S OLD TEDDY. POOR LITTLE JESS. SHE MUST BE FEELING REALLY SCARED AND LONELY.

Later —

I'VE TIED THIS BELL TO YOUR PAL'S COLLAR, SUZIE. NOW IT WON'T BE SO EASY FOR HER TO HIDE. EVERY TIME SHE MOVES SHE'LL JINGLE.

Next morning —

GOOD MORNING, SUZIE. I CAN SEE THAT YOU'RE ALL READY TO GO SHOPPING. I EXPECT YOU'RE LOOKING FORWARD TO VISITING SOME OF THE FRIENDS THAT YOU MADE THE LAST TIME YOU STAYED WITH US.

I'M SURE YOU'LL ENJOY A WALK, TOO, JESS. BUT I'LL HAVE TO KEEP YOU ON A LEAD. CAN'T HAVE YOU GETTING LOST, CAN WE?

But nervous Jess was terrified of traffic noise.

IT'S ALL RIGHT, JESS — NO NEED TO BE SCARED. THE CARS WON'T HURT YOU.

9219 WW02

Suzie had had enough!

OH, SUZIE — NO!

WHY, YOU — AAAH!

HE! HE! HE!

YOU'LL PAY FOR THIS, YOU HORRIBLE ANIMAL!

Suzie completed her rescue safely.

OH, WELL DONE, SUZIE. I'LL PUT JESS ON HER LEAD, THEN WE'LL BEAT A HASTY RETREAT BEFORE MR TOMKINS THINKS OF A WAY TO GET EVEN WITH YOU.

Later —

ROSSI'S

ICE CREAM

DO YOU REMEMBER MR ROSSI'S ICE CREAM PARLOUR, SUZIE? LET'S GO IN AND HAVE AN ICE EACH — I THINK WE ALL DESERVE IT.

But Jess was too nervous to enjoy herself in the cafe.

COME ON, JESS — RELAX. YOU'RE AMONG FRIENDS HERE. NO POINT IN BUYING YOU AN ICE IF YOU'RE GOING TO HIDE YOUR FACE, IS THERE?

Then —

POOR MONKEY DOESN'T HAVE ICE CREAM. HERE, HAVE THIS ONE.

OH, THAT IS KIND OF YOU!

But the toddler's mum didn't agree!

DON'T YOU LET THAT WILD ANIMAL PINCH MY BABY'S ICE CREAM! IT'S A DANGER TO THE PUBLIC!

OH, PLEASE DON'T SHOUT AT JESS. SHE SCARES EASILY.

But Petra's warning came too late!

OH, NO! JESS, COME BACK!

THANK GOODNESS I PUT THAT BELL ON HER COLLAR! AT LEAST WE CAN STILL HEAR HER!

I CAN'T SEE HER BUT I CAN HEAR HER BELL OVER THERE, IN THE MARKET. COME ON, SUZIE — WE'LL SOON CATCH UP WITH HER.

But —

OH, NO — IT WASN'T JESS'S BELL THAT I COULD HEAR, IT WAS A BABY'S RATTLE. JESS COULD BE MILES AWAY BY NOW!

Then —

I SAW YOU IN THE CAFE. IF YOU'VE LOST ONE OF YOUR CHIMPS, I THINK I SAW HER HEADING FOR THE PARK GATES JUST NOW.

OH, THANKS — WHAT A RELIEF!

Soon afterwards —

BOO, OO, OO!

POOR SUZIE — I DO BELIEVE YOU'RE CRYING BECAUSE WE CAN'T SEE ANY SIGN OF JESS IN THE PARK. IF IT'S ANY HELP TO YOU, I WOULDN'T MIND JOINING YOU AND HAVING A GOOD HOWL MYSELF.

Then —

YOU THREW ONE OF MY DOLLS ON THE GROUND BECAUSE I WOULDN'T LET YOU WHEEL MY TWIN PRAM! I'M GOING TO TELL MY MUM ON YOU!

I NEVER WENT NEAR YOUR SILLY PRAM!

Then —

STOP IT, MONKEY! BRING IT BACK!

SUZIE, WHAT ARE YOU DOING? YOU MUSTN'T TAKE THE LITTLE GIRL'S PRAM.

23

But —

JESS! SHE MUST HAVE BEEN FRIGHTENED AND HID IN THERE AND THEN FELL ASLEEP, EXHAUSTED.

JILL HAS BEEN VERY SELFISH WITH THAT PRAM, BUT NOW SHE'S BEING FORCED TO SHARE IT, AND A GOOD THING TOO. WE'LL GIVE YOUR CHIMP A LIFT HOME IN IT, SO YOU DON'T HAVE ANY MORE PROBLEMS, DEAR.

ALL RIGHT — BUT I'M GOING TO PUSH. IT IS MY PRAM.

YOU CAN'T WIN WITH JILL, I'M AFRAID.

Back home Mum had news —

PETRA, THANK GOODNESS YOU'RE BACK! UNCLE JIM'S COLLEAGUE JUST RANG. HE'S OVER HIS ILLNESS AND HE'S COMING TO COLLECT JESS AT ANY MOMENT.

WOW! WHAT A RELIEF!

IT'S SAD FOR YOU, THOUGH, SUZIE, TO BE LOSING YOUR NEW FRIEND SO SOON.

But, when Suzie and the family waved Jess off —

HE! HE! HE!

DO YOU KNOW, SUZIE, I THINK YOU'RE AS RELIEVED AS I AM TO SEE THE BACK OF POOR JESS. HAVING SUCH A NERVOUS FRIEND AROUND MUST HAVE BEEN QUITE A RESPONSIBILITY FOR YOU, TOO!

24

MIDWINTON

"But, with Dad driving, getting there was a big enough problem!"

DAD! WE SHOULD BE HEADING FOR MIDWINTON — YOU'VE TURNED THE WRONG WAY.

LEAVE DAD ALONE, MARY. I'D BE A LOT HAPPIER IF WE *NEVER* REACH MR PALMER'S PLACE!

"Of course, we were late arriving!"

OH, MY GOODNESS! YOU'VE INVITED *THEM*, HENRY? THEY LOOK AWFULLY COMMON!

"The two kids and Mr Palmer seemed friendly enough. Only Mrs Palmer and the guard-dog didn't seem to take to us —"

IT'S OKAY, BABS. THAT'S OLD BUTCH! HE'S QUITE FRIENDLY REALLY.

I'LL TAKE YOUR WORD FOR IT, BOBBY.

"After lunch —"

STAY IN THE GARDEN, CHILDREN, AND *DON'T* DRAG DIRT INTO THE HOUSE!

YES, MOTHER.

"But, during a game of hide-and-seek —"

ONE HUNDRED! WE'RE COMING!

OH, NO! I'M SHRINKING! I'D BETTER STAY HIDDEN UNTIL I GROW AGAIN — I HOPE IT WON'T BE LONG!

"Pinkie just made it!"

CLICK!

IF I CAN JUST GET IN THAT ROOM AND CLOSE THE DOOR BEFORE THE CAT REACHES ME —

PHEW! THE DOOR WAS HEAVY, BUT I DID IT!

"But her troubles weren't over!"

IT'S EMBARRASSING TO THROW THEM OUT LIKE THIS, SARAH. I CAN'T BELIEVE WILMER AND HIS DAUGHTERS ARE THIEVES!

SEE FOR YOURSELF, HENRY! MY JEWELLERY HAS GONE FROM MY DRESSING-TABLE. WHO ELSE WOULD TAKE THEM?

SO THAT'S WHAT IT'S ALL ABOUT! THEY THINK WE'RE THIEVES! OH, NO — THE CAT! I — I'D BETTER CLIMB THE CURTAINS!

"Mr and Mrs Palmer left the room, but Pinkie was trapped!"

THERE'S ONLY ONE THING FOR IT! I'LL HAVE TO CLIMB DOWN THE IVY!

OO-ER! I'M GROWING!

THE BRANCH WON'T HOLD MY WEIGHT — AAGH!

"Pinkie's yells brought the rest of us running."

HOW DARE YOU CLIMB TREES? JUST LOOK WHAT YOU'VE DONE!

SORRY, MRS PALMER. BUT I SPOTTED A MAGPIE, AND I THINK I'VE FOUND SOMETHING INTERESTING!

"Later —"

LOOK AT THIS, MY DEAR! YOUR MISSING JEWELLERY — IN A MAGPIE'S NEST!

YOU *ARE* CLEVER, BABS, DEAR!

"So, we didn't have to leave after all. On Monday morning on our way home —"

WELL, WELL! FANCY MRS PALMER THINKING WE WERE JEWEL THIEVES! BUT I GOT THAT CONTRACT! ALL'S WELL THAT ENDS WELL, EH?

WHY WOULD WE WANT TO STEAL JEWELS ANYWAY? WE'VE GOT DAD — HE'S A *REAL GEM!*

32

The Statue Of Liberty is in –
DENMARK?

Well, this one is!

Made from 1.4 million LEGO bricks, it stands nine metres high and is just one of the amazing miniature monuments which fill the famous LEGOLAND Park in the town of Billund, now visited by around a million visitors a year.

About 33 million LEGO bricks have been used for the many models which grace the Park's Miniland. Buildings, monuments, trains, cars, ships, animals, etc., blend with lovely plants and miniature trees in an area covering some 100,000 square metres.

Besides the models, there are many different activities and amusements for the whole family. There are exciting exhibitions of dolls' houses and toys. There are also nine restaurants and cafeterias.

The Traffic School is one of the most unusual activities. Here children between eight and fourteen can have a twenty minute driving course with an instructor, and are awarded their own LEGOLAND driving licence, when they pass the test.

C

In 1932, Ole Kirk Christiansen, a Danish carpenter and joiner, began making wooden toys. Two years later they were given the name LEGO, derived from "Leg Godt" which is Danish for "Play Well".

In 1949, plastic bricks became part of the LEGO range of toys, which went from strength to strength the world over.

Ole Kirk's son, Godtfred Kirk Christiansen was involved in the work from an early age, and on the death of his father took over the running of the company.

In the mid-sixties he hit on the idea of creating a permanent open-air exhibition of LEGO buildings.

The LEGOLAND park, as the exhibition became known, opened on June 7th, 1968.

A ride through LEGO SAFARI. See lions, tigers, crocodiles, giraffes and many other animals — all made with LEGO bricks!

Castle on the Rhine.

The Interskandinavic Airport.

St. Oluf's Castle (Finland).

Background: Medbourne — an English village.

Mini-world-cruise to see the Wat Phra Keo temple in Bangkok.

The royal Danish residence in Copenhagen (900,000 LEGO bricks and 40,000 window panes!).

Sitting Bull monument. (1.5 million bricks).

Amsterdam.

ROBINA HOOD

IN Sherwood Forest long ago, Robina Hood and her friends, all descendants of Robin Hood and his Merry Men, set out to carry on the noble deeds of their elderly relatives.

THE YOUNG KNIGHT IS SORE ASSAILED, ROBINA!

BY OUR FOES, THE SHERIFF'S GUARDS, FLO TUCK!

SHOOT, WINNIE SCARLET, WHILE FLO AND LITTLE JANE SWING DOWN.

AAAH! YOW! LOOK OUT!

BE OFF OR GET ANOTHER CLOUT!

I AM SIR GARTH GILMOUR. PRITHEE, WHO ARE YOU AND THESE DOUGHTY DAMSELS?

OUTLAWS OF THE GREENWOOD. NOW WHAT MISCHIEF HAVE YOU DONE TO BE UNHORSED AND SET UPON BY THE SHERIFF'S MEN?

I DID BUT SEEK THE SHERIFF'S SEAL OF OFFICE UPON THIS DOCUMENT WHEREBY I MAY INHERIT CERTAIN LANDS IN THE SHIRE OF NOTTINGHAM. TO MY DISMAY THE SHERIFF DEMANDED A PRICE I COULD NOT PAY.

SUCH BRIBERY IS OFT OUR SHERIFF'S KNAVISH WAY!

HE THEN SOUGHT TO SEIZE MY DOCUMENT AS A FORGERY, THUS FORCING ME TO FLEE, PURSUED BY HIS GUARDS.

DOUBTLESS HE PLANS TO CLAIM YOUR LANDS FOR HIMSELF. COME! WE WILL CONSULT OUR ELDERS ON THIS MATTER.

At a forest hideaway—

MEET FRIAR TUCK, LITTLE JOHN, AND MY GRANDSIRE ROBIN.

FORSOOTH, I KNEW NOT THEY WERE ALL STILL LIVING!

OORGH! GADSTEETH! I WISH I WAS NOT!

SECOND FIDDLE *Sarah*

YOUR HEART CAN BE BROKEN IN MANY DIFFERENT WAYS! THIS IS JUST ONE OF THEM!

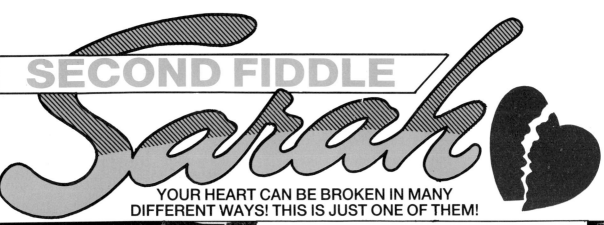

SARAH BRYAN had always played second fiddle to her attractive older sister, Carey. She tried hard not to be jealous, but it wasn't easy!

ANOTHER GOAL! THAT'S THE SECOND ONE CAREY'S SCORED! NO WONDER SHE'S CAPTAIN OF THE TEAM AND FORM CAPTAIN, TOO!

NO NEED TO RUB IT IN, DI. I *HAVE* NOTICED HOW WONDERFUL MY BIG SISTER IS!

I SOMETIMES WONDER IF I EXIST AT ALL, APART FROM BEING CAREY BRYAN'S SISTER.

But the English mistress had a surprise for Sarah—

SARAH, HOW ABOUT AUDITIONING FOR A PART IN THE SCHOOL PLAY?

ME? OOOH! I COULD TRY, MISS HADDEN.

And to Sarah's surprise—

WELL DONE, SARAH! YOU CAN PLAY PAMELA! LEARN YOUR LINES SOON, SO THAT WE CAN REHEARSE PROPERLY.

But then—

CAREY — WHAT ARE YOU DOING HERE?

I HOPE SHE'S NOT GOING TO BE IN THE PLAY, TOO. I THOUGHT FOR ONCE, I'D GET THE LIMELIGHT TO MYSELF.

I'M TO BE DOING THE PROMPTING, SARAH. I'M GLAD YOU'VE GOT SUCH A GOOD PART.

But Sarah found it hard to learn her lines—

IT'S NO GOOD — I'LL NEVER LEARN THIS LOT.

YOU WON'T LEARN LINES WHILE WATCHING TV. WHY DON'T YOU TAKE THE SCRIPT TO YOUR ROOM?

I DON'T NEED YOUR ADVICE THANKS! YOU WOULDN'T BE SO SMUG IF YOU HAD TO LEARN THIS PART.

I ALMOST KNOW IT, AS IT IS, SARAH. WE STUDIED THIS PLAY IN ENGLISH LAST YEAR.

CAREY IS TOO GOOD TO BE TRUE SOMETIMES. I FEEL TOO FED UP TO CARRY ON LINE-LEARNING TONIGHT. I'LL LISTEN TO SOME MUSIC INSTEAD.

Soon, Miss Hadden had had enough of Sarah's laziness, and—

THAT'S IT, SARAH — YOU HAVEN'T MADE THE EFFORT TO LEARN YOUR LINES. I'M ASKING SOMEONE ELSE TO TAKE YOUR PLACE.

BUT THAT'S NOT FAIR — I TRIED, HONESTLY I DID —

And then—

CAREY — YOU CAN TAKE OVER. YOU KNOW MOST OF THE LINES, AND THERE'S NO TIME TO LOOK FOR ANYONE ELSE NOW.

I — I — YES, WELL, ALL RIGHT —

So, next day—

41

Two days later—

GUESS WHAT? DISHY DAN TAYLOR HAS ASKED ME TO GO OUT WITH HIM TONIGHT.

OH YES?

I'LL HAVE TO DO SOMETHING ABOUT THIS. I'M STARTING TO GET AN IDEA ALREADY.

So from a call-box—

CAREY'S BEST FRIEND, SUE, IS HAVING TROUBLE AT HOME AT THE MOMENT. I KNOW THAT CAREY WOULD DROP EVERYTHING IF SUE ASKED HER FOR HELP.

I — I CAN HARDLY TALK FOR CRYING — I HAD AN AWFUL ROW WITH MY FOLKS. CAN YOU COME ROUND TONIGHT?

THE HANDKERCHIEF MUFFLES MY VOICE.

GOOD! SHE BELIEVED THAT WAS SUE AND SHE'S GOING ROUND TO HER PLACE STRAIGHT AWAY.

A few minutes later—

WILL YOU RING DAN AND TELL HIM THAT I CAN'T MAKE IT? HERE'S THE NUMBER. I HAVE TO GO ROUND TO SUE'S PLACE RIGHT AWAY.

YES, OF COURSE I WILL —

But—

CAREY TOLD ME SHE WAS GOING TO MEET DAN AT THE STATION AT SIX. I'LL TELL HIM IN PERSON THEN GET HIM TO TAKE ME OUT INSTEAD.

But when Sarah explained—

I KNOW SUE LEWIS. I'LL GO ROUND TO HER PLACE AND TAKE THEM BOTH OUT. THAT MIGHT CHEER SUE UP A BIT.

DRAT! I DIDN'T EXPECT THAT!

When Sarah arrived back home—

OH SARAH. SUE WASN'T UPSET AT ALL — SHE NEVER MADE THAT TELEPHONE CALL. WHO WOULD PLAY SUCH A TRICK ON ME?

POOR CAREY! WHAT A ROTTEN THING TO HAPPEN.

CAREY'S SO USED TO EVERYTHING GOING RIGHT FOR HER THAT SHE'S KNOCKED OFF HER FEET WHEN THINGS START TO GO WRONG. GOOD!

Next day, after school—

YOU'LL NEVER GUESS WHAT — DAN WENT ROUND TO SUE'S PLACE LAST NIGHT, AND HE TOOK HER OUT, INSTEAD OF ME. I'LL NEVER TRUST EITHER OF THEM AGAIN.

NOW HER WORLD'S STARTING TO FALL APART, JUST AS MINE DID WHEN SHE TOOK THE PART IN THE PLAY AWAY FROM ME.

But, a few days later—

CAREY, LOVE, WE'VE GOT YOU A NEW BIKE. MUM AND I SAW IT IN A SALE, AND WE REMEMBERED THAT YOU HAD ALMOST OUTGROWN YOUR OLD ONE.

OH THAT IS KIND OF YOU BOTH — I DON'T KNOW WHAT TO SAY —

WE HAVEN'T FORGOTTEN YOU, EITHER, SARAH. YOU CAN HAVE CAREY'S OLD BIKE. I KNOW THAT YOU LIKE TINKERING WITH THINGS, SO I'VE BOUGHT YOU A REPAIR MANUAL. HAVE A GO AT FIXING IT YOURSELF.

OH GREAT — THANKS A BUNDLE, DAD —

WHY SHOULD I HAVE TO REPAIR THIS OLD BONESHAKER WHEN CAREY'S GOT A BRAND NEW BIKE? MUM AND DAD FAVOUR HER ALL THE TIME.

HELLO, SARAH — HAVE YOU FINISHED FIXING THE BIKE ALREADY?

YES, IT WAS A PIECE OF CAKE TO SOMEONE WHO'S MECHANICALLY MINDED, LIKE ME.

I WON'T TELL HER THAT I'VE GIVEN UP ON THE STUPID THING.

Then—

I'LL LET THE TYRES DOWN ON HER NEW BIKE NOW. THAT'LL MAKE HER LATE FOR HER TENNIS TOURNAMENT.

Later—

OH, CAREY SAID TO TELL YOU THAT SHE'S BORROWED YOUR BIKE. IT SEEMS THAT THE TYRES ON HERS WERE FLAT.

WHAT? B-BUT THE BRAKES ON MINE AREN'T WORKING — IT ISN'T SAFE — I MUST TRY TO CATCH HER —

But Sarah was too late—

MR AND MR BRYAN? I'M AFRAID THAT CAREY HAS HAD AN ACCIDENT. SHE CAME OFF HER BIKE AT THE BOTTOM OF DALTON HILL. THEY'VE TAKEN HER TO HOSPITAL.

NO — OH, NO!

Later, at the hospital—

H-HELLO, SARAH — I DON'T KNOW WHAT HAPPENED. I TRIED TO BRAKE AND I COULDN'T STOP. I KNOW THAT YOU HAD FIXED THE BIKE — YOU SAID SO —

OH CAREY, I'M SO SORRY! I — I HAVE TO TALK TO MUM AND DAD —

I HAVE TO TELL THEM THE TRUTH. I CAN'T LIVE WITH ALL THIS GUILT.

So, Sarah told her parents about the tricks she had been playing on Carey.

IT'S NO GOOD CRYING CROCODILE TEARS AND ASKING US TO FORGIVE YOU. CAREY COULD HAVE BEEN KILLED ON THAT BIKE. IT'S GOING TO TAKE A LONG TIME FOR US TO FORGET THIS, SARAH.

HAS IT EVER OCCURRED TO YOU THAT THE REASON CAREY SUCCEEDS IS THAT SHE'S A TRIER AND SHE KNOWS HOW TO LOSE GRACIOUSLY AS WELL AS HOW TO WIN?

BECAUSE OF MY JEALOUSY AND PETTINESS I'VE PUT MY SISTER IN HOSPITAL — AND I'VE LOST THE TRUST OF EVERYONE THAT I CARE FOR MOST. I FEEL AS THOUGH MY HEART IS BREAKING — AND I KNOW THAT I DESERVE IT.

WHO IS

Sylvie Guillem has the world at her feet!

In 1989, the French ballerina joined the Royal Ballet as principal guest artiste. The contract was signed on her twenty-fourth birthday, and bound her to give at least twenty-five performances a year for three years.

Sylvie is only the third long-term guest to be signed up in Royal Ballet history, after Natalia Makarova and Rudolf Nureyev. At twenty-two, she was also the youngest guest ever engaged by the Royal Ballet.

A protegée of Nureyev's, she is tipped to be one of the main influences in ballet for the next decade. Equally at home in classical or contemporary roles,

she is a rare combination of suppleness and strength.

She has the kind of physique that dance schools are always searching for, and her phenomenal technique makes the most difficult manoeuvres look easy, and brings beauty and finesse to even the simplest linking steps. She is famous for her long legs, and her incredible 180 degree elevations, as seen below, are a feature of her dancing never to be forgotten.

Sylvie was born in Paris. At the age of eleven she was training to be a gymnast when she took a course at the Paris Opera Ballet school, which she then joined.

In 1981 she entered the corps de ballet as a "quadrille" or supporting dancer. In 1983 she won the gold medal at the famous Varna Competition. After winning another top award, the Carpeaux Prize in 1984, she was promoted to one of the top positions, "premiere danseuse" with the company.

Then just five days later, she became the leading dancer or "etoile" with the company, after a superb performance of Swan Lake. Her promotion was announced during the curtain calls for the performance, amidst tumultuous applause

and showers of flowers! She was just nineteen!

Since then she has danced all over the world as a special guest dancer, visiting such places as Seychelles, Helsinki, Hamburg, Stuttgart, Copenhagen, Peking and Japan, besides giving regular performances for French ballet.

Sylvie's early decision to become a ballerina rather than a gymnast must have been a difficult one, particularly as her mother was her gym teacher. But anyone seeing her dance today will soon tell you that her decision was the right one!

DESIGN A FASHION

The eight lucky winners who drew these designs have each won £5. YOU could be a winner, too, if you enter our Design A Fashion competition in the weekly Bunty magazine!

1. Lorna Anderson, Dunlop.
2. Karena Richardson, Luton.

3. Gwen McGinty, Rutherglen.
4. Cynthia Fern, Rochdale.
5. Wendy Tweed, Portstewart.

6. Sarah Bowie, Dun-Loaire.
7. Janine MacDonald, Stornoway.
8. Yolanda Taw, Mitcham.

THE COMP

A DISCO? MEGA! BUT WHAT'LL I WEAR?

I KNOW, EVERYONE BRING YOUR GEAR ROUND TO MY HOUSE TONIGHT. WE'LL WORK OUT WHAT TO PUT ON.

And so, later—

SO LET ME GET THIS STRAIGHT, BECKY'S WEARING LAURA'S LEGGINGS AND MY TOP, I'M WEARING BECKY'S DRESS, LAURA'S WEARING MY SKIRT AND T-SHIRT, AND HAYLEY . . .

I'M WEARING MY OWN CLOTHES, ACTUALLY!

HA! HA!

THAT WAS A LAUGH, WASN'T IT? HEY, WHAT'S UP, BECKY? YOU'VE NOT BEEN YOURSELF TONIGHT.

I'M REALLY WORRIED ABOUT MY REPORT CARD, HAYLEY. MUM SAID LAST TIME IF I DIDN'T IMPROVE, I'D BE IN TROUBLE.

YOU'LL DO OKAY. COME ON, HERE'S OUR BUS.

BUS STOP

EVERYONE SAYS IT'LL BE OKAY, BUT IT WON'T — I KNOW IT!

Next day—

LISTEN, GIRLS, IT'S BEEN DECIDED TO HAVE AN 'OLD TIME DANCING' SECTION AT THE DISCO. SO TODAY, YOU'RE GOING TO HAVE INSTRUCTION IN HOW TO DO IT.

YOU'RE JOKING, MISS!

OH, NO!

WHAT AN EMBARRASSMENT!

50

SMILE! IT'S NOT THE END OF THE WORLD!

JUST ABOUT!

LET'S GO GET IT OVER WITH.

I WONDER WHO'LL BE TEACHING US?

DUNNO.

LOOK!

I DON'T BELIEVE IT!

NOW, EVERYONE, PAY ATTENTION, AND MR BARTLETT AND I WILL SHOW YOU HOW TO DANCE PROPERLY.

WE'LL SHOW YOU THE WALTZ FIRST OF ALL . . .

LOOK AT THEM!

I CAN'T! I CAN'T! OLD GRIM GERTIE, AND BASHER BARTLETT!

NOW IT'S YOUR TURN, BOYS. COME ON, YOU FIRST.

HAVE MERCY, SIR!

THIS IS A HOOT, ISN'T IT?

NOT HALF!

Later—

1, 2, 3 AND TURN!

FEET TOGETHER!

STRAIGHTEN THAT BACK!

MUM SAYS SHE'LL GIVE ME A FIVER IF I GET A DECENT REPORT.

MINE'S GOING TO BE ROTTEN, I JUST KNOW IT.

STOP WORRYING! MUM WON'T MIND.

At the next class—

WELL, I HOPE YOU'LL FIND THESE AS AMUSING AS YOUR LAST CLASS.

OH, NO, OUR REPORT CARDS!

But—

THIS JUST ISN'T GOOD ENOUGH, BECKY. I TOLD YOU LAST TIME ABOUT BUCKING UP AT SCHOOL. NO END-OF-TERM DISCO FOR YOU!

BUT, MUM . . .

I'M SORRY, HAYLEY, BUT IT JUST ISN'T ON. SHE JUST DOESN'T DESERVE IT.

STILL, IT WOULD BE NICE TO BE ASKED . . .

Next morning—

I'LL DO BETTER NEXT TERM, HONEST.

I'M SORRY, BECKY, I'VE MADE UP MY MIND.

POOR BECKY, IT LOOKS LIKE MUM'S DETERMINED.

At school—

I CAN JUST SEE ME AND ADAM NOW . . .

GIVE IT A REST, ROZ!

I CAN'T WAIT FOR TOMORROW NIGHT.

I CAN!

Next evening—

HAVE YOU HEARD? THEY'VE DECIDED NOT TO BOTHER WITH THE OLD-TIME DANCING. THANK GOODNESS FOR THAT.

YEAH, GREAT NEWS.

NOT GETTING READY FOR THE DISCO, BECKY?

WHAT DO YOU MEAN?

A Saddle for Strawberry

SALLY SAUNDERS loved horses, but she had no pony of her own. Her friend, Marie Compton, had a pony and sometimes let Sally ride him.

CAN I CANTER HIM, MARIE?

OKAY, BUT DON'T LET HIM CHARGE OFF. I'VE SPENT AGES WORKING ON HIS SCHOOLING.

GOOD BOY, OFF WE GO!

I WISH I COULD HAVE A PONY OF MY OWN, BUT DAD AND MUM JUST HAVEN'T GOT ENOUGH MONEY TO BUY ME ONE.

A little later—

I REALLY ENJOYED THAT, MARIE. STAR'S A SUPER PONY!

I KNOW, HE'S A REAL WINNER, TOO. HE'S WON LOTS OF CUPS AND I INTEND TO WIN SOME MORE. YOU CAN COME ALONG AND HELP WHEN WE GO TO A SHOW IF YOU LIKE.

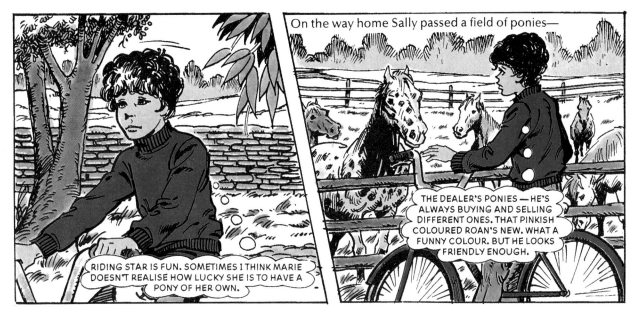

RIDING STAR IS FUN. SOMETIMES I THINK MARIE DOESN'T REALISE HOW LUCKY SHE IS TO HAVE A PONY OF HER OWN.

On the way home Sally passed a field of ponies—

THE DEALER'S PONIES — HE'S ALWAYS BUYING AND SELLING DIFFERENT ONES. THAT PINKISH COLOURED ROAN'S NEW. WHAT A FUNNY COLOUR. BUT HE LOOKS FRIENDLY ENOUGH.

COME ON THEN — HAVE A MINT.

Suddenly, the other ponies charged up—

HEY, GET BACK, YOU LOT!

THE OTHER PONIES DON'T SEEM TO LIKE HIM. I WONDER IF IT'S BECAUSE OF HIS FUNNY COLOUR?

POOR ROAN! I'LL COME AND SEE HIM AGAIN.

When Sally got home—

HI, MUM. YOU LOOK HAPPY! WHAT'S UP, DAD?

WE'VE HAD A BIT OF LUCK. ONE OF OUR PREMIUM BONDS HAS COME UP. IT ISN'T A FORTUNE, BUT THERE'S ENOUGH TO BUY A NEW COOKER, AND GET A NEWER CAR.

THAT'S WONDERFUL, DAD!

YOU'RE TO GET SOMETHING TOO, SALLY. WHAT WOULD YOU LIKE — A NEW BIKE?

OH, DAD, COULD I HAVE A PONY? JUST A CHEAP ONE FROM THE DEALER'S?

THERE'S ENOUGH MONEY FOR A CHEAP PONY, BUT WHAT ABOUT ALL ITS EQUIPMENT— SHOES, A SADDLE AND ALL THE OTHER THINGS PONIES NEED?

I COULD EARN MONEY FOR SHOES, AND RIDE BAREBACK!

OKAY, IF IT'S WHAT YOU WANT, WE'LL GIVE IT A GO. BUT IF YOU CAN'T COPE, THEN THE PONY WILL HAVE TO BE SOLD.

So, the next day—

MOST OF MY PONIES ARE A LOT DEARER THAN WHAT YOU'RE OFFERING, LASS.

PLEASE, MR GRANT, HAVEN'T YOU ANYTHING?

Just then—

THEY'RE CHASING THAT ROAN AGAIN — NONE OF THE OTHER HORSES LIKE HIM. I'LL NOT SELL HIM EASILY.

IS IT BECAUSE OF HIS COLOUR, OR IS HE NASTY?

NO, HE'S NOT NASTY, BUT HE WON'T WIN ANY CUPS FOR HIS LOOKS! NOW HE'D BE CHEAP— SHALL I GET HIM IN?

YES, PLEASE. I DON'T MIND ABOUT HIS LOOKS.

Soon—

I JUST WANT A PONY I CAN RIDE AND LOVE.

WELL, WHAT DO YOU THINK?

60

At Marie's house—

THERE, THAT'S THE SADDLE FITTING FINE.

IT'S LOVELY, ISN'T IT, SALLY? NOW WHAT ABOUT ONE FOR STRAWBERRY?

MM, THIS ONE WILL NEED A SPECIAL SADDLE IF IT'S TO FIT PERFECTLY. I COULD FIND YOU SOMETHING SECOND-HAND FOR ABOUT £150.

THAT WOULD TAKE ME YEARS TO EARN, AND WHAT I DO EARN I NEED FOR STRAWBERRY'S KEEP.

When the saddler left—

SO YOUR HORSE IS A FUNNY SHAPE, EH?

NO, HE'S NOT—THE SADDLER ONLY SAID HE NEEDED TO BE IN BETTER CONDITION. I'LL HAVE HIM IN AS GOOD A SHAPE AS STAR IN NO TIME!

SOME HOPES. HE'S JUST A MISFIT!

STRAWBERRY ISN'T A MISFIT. ONE OF THESE DAYS HE'LL BE WINNING CUPS, WAIT AND SEE!

YOU'VE GOT TO BE KIDDING, SALLY. I TELL YOU, IF THAT MISFIT OF YOURS EVER WINS A CUP, I'LL GIVE YOU ONE OF MY SADDLES!

YOU'RE ON, MARIE! COME ON, STRAWBERRY, IT'S TIME WE WENT HOME.

I'M GOING TO SHOW MARIE—IF IT'S THE LAST THING I DO!

DON'T WORRY, I WON'T LET YOU STAY A JOKE FOR LONG.

Two weeks later—

STRAWBERRY NEEDS WEEKS OF SCHOOLING, BUT IT'S VERY HARD TO DO IT PROPERLY WITHOUT A SADDLE.

STRAWBERRY'S JUMPING ISN'T UP TO MUCH EITHER. I REALLY DO NEED A SADDLE.

I'M GOING TO BUY A HORSE MAGAZINE, AND SEE WHAT LOCAL SHOWS ARE COMING UP.

Sally sent off for some schedules—

NOVICE JUMPING, BEST CHILD'S PONY, WORKING PONY— STRAWBERRY ISN'T READY FOR ANY OF THESE YET, AND ANYWAY, I'D NEED A SADDLE.

The next one sounded better—

THIS IS BETTER, STRAWBERRY — BAREBACK JUMPING, TWO FEET HIGH, AND FAMILY PONY. WE COULD TRY BOTH OF THOSE — SURELY A FAMILY PONY COULD BE RIDDEN BAREBACK.

Sally practised hard—

THAT'S BETTER STRAWBERRY.

NOT HAVING TO TRY TO JUMP ANY HIGHER THAN TWO FEET IS GIVING US BOTH CONFIDENCE.

PRACTISING FOR THE OPEN JUMPING, SALLY? THEY DON'T GIVE CUPS FOR WINNING THE OBSTACLE RACE! HA! HA!

YOU WAIT, MARIE, STRAWBERRY AND I ARE GOING TO SURPRISE YOU. WE'LL BE AT THE LOWTON SHOW ON SATURDAY, JUST LIKE YOU.

OH, WELL, I'LL BE WATCHING. IT SHOULD BE A REAL LAUGH!

On Saturday morning—

But Sally discovered that more than a clear round was needed—

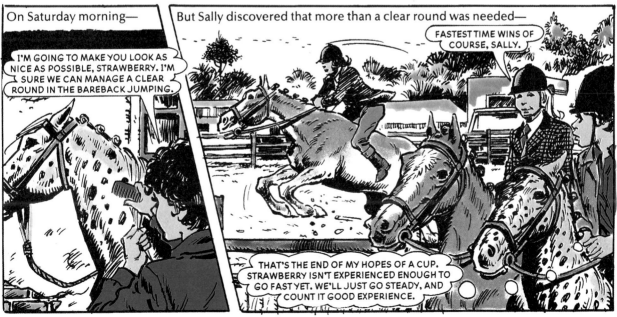

I'M GOING TO MAKE YOU LOOK AS NICE AS POSSIBLE, STRAWBERRY. I'M SURE WE CAN MANAGE A CLEAR ROUND IN THE BAREBACK JUMPING.

FASTEST TIME WINS OF COURSE, SALLY.

THAT'S THE END OF MY HOPES OF A CUP. STRAWBERRY ISN'T EXPERIENCED ENOUGH TO GO FAST YET. WE'LL JUST GO STEADY, AND COUNT IT GOOD EXPERIENCE.

And so—

GOOD BOY, WELL DONE!

Sally didn't win a cup, but—

A ROSETTE FOR A CLEAR ROUND—THAT'S GREAT! IT MAY NOT WIN ME MARIE'S SADDLE, BUT I'LL ALWAYS BE PROUD OF IT.

In the family pony class—

FAMILY PONIES HAVE TO BE SAFE AND SENSIBLE. STRAWBERRY'S THAT, BUT I'M AFRAID HIS LOOKS MAY SPOIL HIS CHANCE OF WINNING ANYTHING.

But Strawberry won a rosette—

A GOOD EFFORT—HE'S A VERY SAFE FAMILY PONY. BUT HE DOES NEED MORE SCHOOLING.

When Sally was getting ready to go home—

AND NOW THE WINNER OF OUR SPECIAL AWARD, A CUP FOR THE COMPETITOR WHO HAS PUT THE MOST EFFORT INTO COMPETING HERE TODAY. THE WINNER IS SALLY SAUNDERS.

THAT'S *YOU*—YOU'VE WON A CUP!

CONGRATULATIONS, SALLY, WE HOPE TO SEE YOU AGAIN.

WELL, WHO'D HAVE BELIEVED IT? IT LOOKS LIKE I'M GOING TO HAVE TO KEEP MY SIDE OF THE WAGER.

So, next day—

I DON'T THINK I'D BETTER LAUGH AT STRAWBERRY ANY MORE. YOU DESERVE MY SADDLE, SALLY.

THANKS, MARIE. MAYBE SOME DAY STRAWBERRY AND I WILL BE ABLE TO GIVE EVEN YOU AND STAR SOME COMPETITION!

PENNY PRESTON'S father was an artist, and Penny was used to life in a cluttered studio flat in London. Then Dominic Preston sold a painting for a large sum of money, and decided it was time to move to more artistic surroundings in the country . . .

PERFECT! THIS IS JUST WHAT I'M LOOKING FOR!

IT LOOKS SUPER, DAD. LET'S TAKE A LOOK INSIDE.

The Painting

Some time later —

THIS ROOM'S FABULOUS. IMAGINE IT IN WINTER, WITH A LOG FIRE BURNING!

YES! AND THERE'S MEANT TO BE A ROOM UPSTAIRS WITH A DECENT NORTH LIGHT FOR MY PAINTING.

YES, PENNY, THIS IS THE PLACE. I SHALL PAINT HERE, BETTER THAN I'VE EVER PAINTED BEFORE!

DAD CAN BE DIFFICULT TO LIVE WITH, ESPECIALLY SINCE MUM DIED. THIS COULD BE JUST THE PLACE HE NEEDS TO RELAX IN.

But just before they drove away —

THAT'S STRANGE! SUDDENLY IT'S NOT NEARLY SO BRIGHT AND PRETTY. THERE MUST BE A CLOUD OVER THE SUN OR SOMETHING. WHAT AN ODD ILLUSION!

Penny and her father moved in, and on the first morning —

HOW LOVELY! THE BIRDS AND ANIMALS MUST HAVE BECOME USED TO THE PEOPLE WHO LIVED HERE BEFORE.

HOLD IT JUST LIKE THAT, PENNY, WHILE I FIND MY SKETCH PAD.

ALL THE CREATURES ARE REALLY TAME. IT'S MARVELLOUS!

THAT'S FINE, PENNY! KEEP THEM THERE!

DAD'S GETTING REALLY CARRIED AWAY! I COULD BE HERE ALL MORNING!

But then —

DRAT!

THAT CAT'S SPOILED EVERYTHING!

66

THERE YOU ARE, PENNY! HURRY UP WITH THE MEAL. I'LL HAVE TO GO TO TOWN THIS AFTERNOON. I'M OUT OF YELLOW OCHRE. I THOUGHT I HAD A FULL TUBE YESTERDAY.

I'LL GET US SOME LUNCH NOW.

DAD'S CROSS! HE HATES TO BE INTERRUPTED.

After lunch —

THERE ARE TWO BUTTONS MISSING FROM MY BEST SHIRT. YOU KNOW I CAN'T SEW BUTTONS ON! YOUR MOTHER WOULD HAVE NOTICED . . .

OH, DAD! COULDN'T YOU WEAR YOUR BLUE ONE?

IT ISN'T REALLY HIS BEST SHIRT. HE'S JUST FEELING IRRITABLE.

I SUPPOSE I'LL HAVE TO! FIRST MY YELLOW OCHRE, NOW MY SHIRT. I SHOULD HAVE KNOWN THINGS WERE TOO GOOD TO LAST.

A little later —

I'LL TIDY UP IN THE GARDEN WHILE DAD'S OUT. WHY, WHAT'S THE MATTER WITH THE BIRDS? THEY SEEM SCARED!

Suddenly —

OOOH! THAT SQUIRREL LOOKS ANGRY! I ALMOST THOUGHT IT WAS ATTACKING ME!

70

AND LOOK AT THIS, THE PLANTS ARE RUINED AND THE FISH HAVE DIED! THIS IS CREEPY!

I TOLD YOU! IF THERE BE HARSH WORDS, THE BEAUTY WILL FAIL, THE PAINTER MAN DROVE AWAY! MY CATS HAD TO RUN. THIS IS AS IT WILL BE, ALL DYING AND DECAY. HOW IT IS IN THE OTHER PAINTER MAN'S HEART — UNTIL THERE IS HAPPINESS, AND A SUNNY CANVAS!

OH! I DIDN'T KNOW ANYONE WAS THERE. WHAT DO YOU MEAN? DID SOMEONE DO ALL THIS?

YES! IT IS ALL DECAYING . . .

PLEASE, CAN'T YOU EXPLAIN TO ME PROPERLY WHAT'S HAPPENING?

But —

EXPLAIN? YOUR OWN HEART WILL EXPLAIN! LOOK IN THE LOFT.

THE LOFT? THE PAINTING? BUT HOW CAN THAT HAVE ANYTHING TO DO WITH THE DEAD POND?

I MUST HAVE ANOTHER LOOK OR I'LL FEEL CREEPY ALL NIGHT!

And when Penny looked at the painting —

OH, NO! THE PAINTING SEEMS TO HAVE CHANGED! IT LOOKS EVEN WORSE THAN IT DID BEFORE! I'M GETTING SCARED. IT'S AS IF THERE'S A CURSE ON OUR COTTAGE SOMEHOW! BUT WHAT CAN I DO?

THERE'S DAD CALLING. I WON'T TELL HIM ABOUT THIS! HE'D ONLY THINK IT WAS NONSENSE. HE MIGHT EVEN DESTROY THIS PAINTING OR SOMETHING, AND I'VE GOT A FEELING THAT GETTING ANGRY AND SMASHING IT MIGHT BE THE WORST THING WE COULD DO.

BEEN EXPLORING THE ROOF, PENNY? ANYTHING INTERESTING IN THERE?

ONLY BIRDS' NESTS, DAD.

HE'S IN A GOOD MOOD AGAIN NOW. I THOUGHT HE'D ENJOY A TRIP OUT. BUT EACH TIME HE'S BEEN CROSS, OR I HAVE, SOMETHING SEEMS TO CHANGE ROUND THE COTTAGE. IS THAT WHAT ABEL MEANT? THE COTTAGE WILL ONLY THRIVE IF WE ARE GOOD-TEMPERED?

URGH! WEAK TEA, PENNY . . .

SORRY, DAD! I'LL MAKE YOU SOME MORE!

IT'S NOT THAT WEAK, BUT I WON'T RISK STARTING AN ARGUMENT!

And later —

HONESTLY! THIS FELLOW SHAW DOESN'T KNOW THE FIRST THING ABOUT WATER COLOURS.

I'VE BEEN LOOKING AT THIS CATALOGUE FROM THE GARDEN CENTRE. YOU KNOW YOU LOVE HERBS IN FOOD. WHAT ABOUT BUYING THEIR SPECIAL KIT?

IF HE STARTS GETTING CROSS ABOUT WHAT MR SHAW SAYS ABOUT PAINTING, IT MIGHT LEAD TO TROUBLE.

By bedtime —

WELL, I DON'T KNOW IF I HELPED IN ANY WAY BY BEING SO CAREFUL WITH DAD, BUT I DO KNOW IT'S JOLLY TIRING! BUT CAN I FIND A PERMANENT SOLUTION TO ALL THIS?

Next morning —

OH, NO, JUST WHAT I DON'T NEED! MY WRETCHED SISTER DORCAS AND HER OBNOXIOUS BROOD ARE GOING TO VISIT US THIS AFTERNOON! HOW CAN I WORK WITH THEM UNDERFOOT?

THIS SOUNDS DANGEROUS. DAD AND HIS SISTER HAVE NEVER GOT ON! THERE'S SURE TO BE A ROW. I'M GOING TO HAVE MY WORK CUT OUT KEEPING THE PEACE THIS AFTERNOON.

OH, DAD!

NOW HE'S CROSS AGAIN, AND HE'S SCARED THE BIRDS.

And when Penny came out a little later —

OH, NO!

BLACKBIRDS ATTACKING ME JUST LIKE THAT SQUIRREL DID. EVEN THE CREATURES ARE AFFECTED BY ARGUMENTS, OR ANGER. IT REALLY IS AS IF THERE'S A CURSE OR AN ENCHANTMENT ON ROSE COTTAGE.

Later, in the village shop —

E. NESBIT

THAT'S THE LOT THEN, IS IT, LASS? I WONDER, SINCE YOU'RE NEIGHBOURS, COULD YOU TAKE THIS BAG TO OLD ABEL. HE HASN'T BEEN IN FOR A DAY OR SO.

OPEN

YES, ALL RIGHT.

OH, DEAR, I'M A BIT SCARED OF MR HONEYMAN. BUT PERHAPS I CAN GET HIM TO TELL ME MORE ABOUT OUR COTTAGE.

CARTER'S FINEST MILK CHOCOLATE

SO THIS IS WHERE ABEL LIVES. IT'S NOT THAT FAR FROM OUR COTTAGE.

THE FRAME'S ALL SWOLLEN, AS IF IT WAS REALLY NEGLECTED, BUT I KNOW IT WAS ALL RIGHT THIS MORNING! THIS IS REALLY FRIGHTENING!

Penny climbed into the loft —

I CAN'T SEE ANOTHER CANVAS. AND THOSE BIRDS SOUND ANGRY. I'VE UPSET THEM, SEARCHING AROUND HERE. ALL THIS ANGER . . .

Suddenly —

THERE'S THE EASEL. IT ALMOST LOOKS AS IF IT WAS LEFT THERE ON PURPOSE FOR SOMEONE TO FIND. WHAT DID ABEL SAY, FINISH THE PAIR. I WISH I COULD WORK THIS OUT!

PERHAPS IT MEANS I SHOULD DO ANOTHER PAINTING — THE REVERSE OF THE HORRIBLE ONE! WOULD THAT STOP ROSE COTTAGE FALLING APART? IT'S WORTH A TRY!

And so —

THE COTTAGE FIRST, BRIGHT AND FRESH AS I CAN. I CAN'T PAINT LIKE DAD, BUT I CAN DO MY BEST!

75

OH, DAD!

WELL, PERHAPS DORCAS WASN'T SO FAR OUT. LOOK HOW IT'S GONE. IT'LL TAKE A GREAT DEAL OF WORK TO PUT THE PLACE TO RIGHT.

And so, that night —

MY PICTURE! I MUST FINISH IT! IT'S THE ONLY CHANCE. I'LL PAINT IT AS IT SHOULD BE —

And just before dawn —

A few hours later —

I'VE DONE IT! I'VE PAINTED THE SECOND PICTURE, BUT WILL IT WORK?

IT'S LIGHT, AND THAT'S DAD CALLING! HE SOUNDS EXCITED.

I MUST HAVE BEEN IMAGINING THINGS LAST NIGHT, THINKING THE COTTAGE WAS IN SUCH A STATE. AMAZING WHAT PEOPLE CAN PUT IN YOUR MINDS — DORCAS ALWAYS COULD UPSET ME. AND BY THE WAY, THERE WAS A NOTE FROM OLD ABEL, WRITTEN BY ONE OF THE NURSES. HE'S GETTING WELL, AND HE SAID TO REMEMBER ABOUT THE PAINTING. HE DIDN'T MEAN TO GIVE A KIND GIRL SUCH TROUBLE, WHATEVER THAT MEANS. BUT THERE HAD TO BE A PAIR. WHATEVER IS HE ON ABOUT?

I THINK I KNOW, DAD! BUT IT'S ALL RIGHT NOW! IN FACT I THINK EVERYTHING'S ALL RIGHT NOW!

THAT WAS THE ANSWER — FOR SOMEONE WHO WAS HAPPY HERE TO FINISH THE PAIR OF PAINTINGS. THE CURSE HAS BEEN LIFTED. ROSE COTTAGE IS SAFE!

LEADING

If you've ever seen American Football on T.V., you'll have seen the Cheer Leaders! These are those energetic girls who prance around in well-rehearsed routines chanting encouragement to the teams!

Cheer Leaders are a way of life in many American schools, and it's every young girl's ambition to become one.

Newport High School in California is a typical example. Since 1935 there have always been Cheer Leaders at the school.

Training starts in Junior School when the girls are nine, so by the time they reach High School, they're twelve and have had lots of practice. The Cheer Leaders at Newport High range from twelve to fifteen years old.

The training of a Cheer Leader is mighty tough. Hundreds of girls try out for around thirty places!

Each girl has to make up a two-minute routine which she performs before experienced Cheer Leaders. The numbers are whittled down to a hundred, then to fifty then to the final thirty.

Final auditions take place on the school campus before hundreds of spectators, and professionals are invited

LADIES!

along to watch and judge the auditions, which often take hours. The winners will join one of Newport High's three squads of dancers. So it's a nerve-wracking experience for those involved.

It's a costly business for the parents of the chosen girls too! Each girl requires several costumes — which can cost their parents up to a thousand dollars. There are different uniforms for football, basketball, hockey and also fun costumes which are worn on other special occasions.

Other items like batons and muffs are required from time to time, and with added travelling expenses the parents hands are seldom out of their pockets. Fund raising events are held regularly to defray the costs.

Besides appearing at sports events, the Cheer Leaders appear at other school activities when required. Many of these events last for two or three hours, and in that time the Cheer Leaders will be on their feet several times performing their routines.

So while there's a lot of glamour in being a Cheer Leader, any of the girls will tell you it's very hard work too!

G'Day! Has anybody here seen Kylie?

They'll never find me behind this tree!

Now where did I leave the car?

There's just nothing in the sales this year!

WHATEVER NECKST?

Having a swinging time!

Fish, fish, fish — nothing but fish!

The Four Marys

MARY RADLEIGH, Mary Simpson, Mary Cotter and Mary Field were best friends at St. Elmo's School for Girls. One of their earliest adventures at the school involved the pretty stream that flowed through the grounds, to join the River Moyle near Elmbury. It all started one day when they took Miss Brooker, a temporary student-teacher, to see the stream . . .

MIND YOUR HEAD, MISS BROOKER. IT'S A BIT OF A SCRAMBLE THROUGH HERE.

IF THERE ARE AS MANY UNUSUAL WATER-PLANTS AS YOU SAY, GROWING AROUND THE STREAM, IT'LL BE WORTH IT.

OH, NO! WHAT'S HAPPENED TO OUR LOVELY STREAM? IT'S BARELY A TRICKLE.

IT CAN'T HAVE DRIED UP! IT'S BEEN ONE OF THE WETTEST TERMS ON RECORD.

IN FACT HERE COMES THE NEXT SHOWER. LET'S GET BACK TO SCHOOL BEFORE WE'RE SOAKED THROUGH.

F

83

84

85

Several hours later —

I'M FED UP WAITING HERE TO BE RESCUED.

THERE'S A BOAT! IF I COULD SCRAMBLE DOWN ON THE ROOF, I MIGHT BE ABLE TO GRAB HOLD OF IT.

BE CAREFUL, SIMPY!

GOT IT! COME ON DOWN!

HEY, ISN'T THAT CHRISTOBEL BAGGSHOTT'S MINI, STRANDED ON THE BRIDGE?

SHE'S STILL IN IT!

Christobel got out of her car.

COME AND RESCUE ME AT ONCE! DON'T JUST STARE AT ME, YOU FOOLS!

HUH! CHARMING AS EVER!

But, then—

OH, NO! THE WATER'S SWEPT AWAY THE BRIDGE!

FIELDY — THAT WAS THE MOST WONDERFUL THING YOU'VE EVER DONE — BUT THE MOST INCREDIBLY STUPID, TOO!

IT'S THE SOLDIERS FROM THE ARMY CAMP, COMING TO RESCUE US. WE'LL BE ALL RIGHT NOW. THANK GOODNESS.

For the next few days the Four Marys were confined to the school medical room.

YOU'LL BE GLAD TO KNOW THAT I'M LETTING YOU GET UP. YOU'RE WANTED IN THE HEAD'S STUDY AS SOON AS YOU'RE DRESSED.

SIR OSCAR WISHES TO THANK YOU, GIRLS — ESPECIALLY MARY FIELD — FOR SAVING HIS DAUGHTER'S LIFE.

IF YOU REALLY MEAN THAT, HOW ABOUT LETTING US HAVE OUR STREAM BACK? YOU KNOW, THE ONE YOU DAMMED TO FILL UP YOUR LAKE!

IF THERE'S ANYTHING YOU WANT, MY DEAR, YOU HAVE ONLY TO NAME IT.

OH, NO! I HOPE THEY DON'T THINK FIELDY'S BEING CHEEKY!

IF IT HADN'T BEEN FOR MY STUPIDITY IN BLOCKING THE STREAM IN THE FIRST PLACE, THE MOYLE MIGHT NEVER HAVE BURST ITS BANKS. REST ASSURED I SHALL NOT REPEAT THE EXERCISE.

THE SUN'S COMING OUT, GIRLS. IT'S EVEN STOPPED RAINING.

THANKS TO FIELDY, WHEN THE WATER'S FINALLY GONE DOWN, OUR STREAM WILL FLOW THROUGH THE GROUNDS OF ST ELMO'S AGAIN.

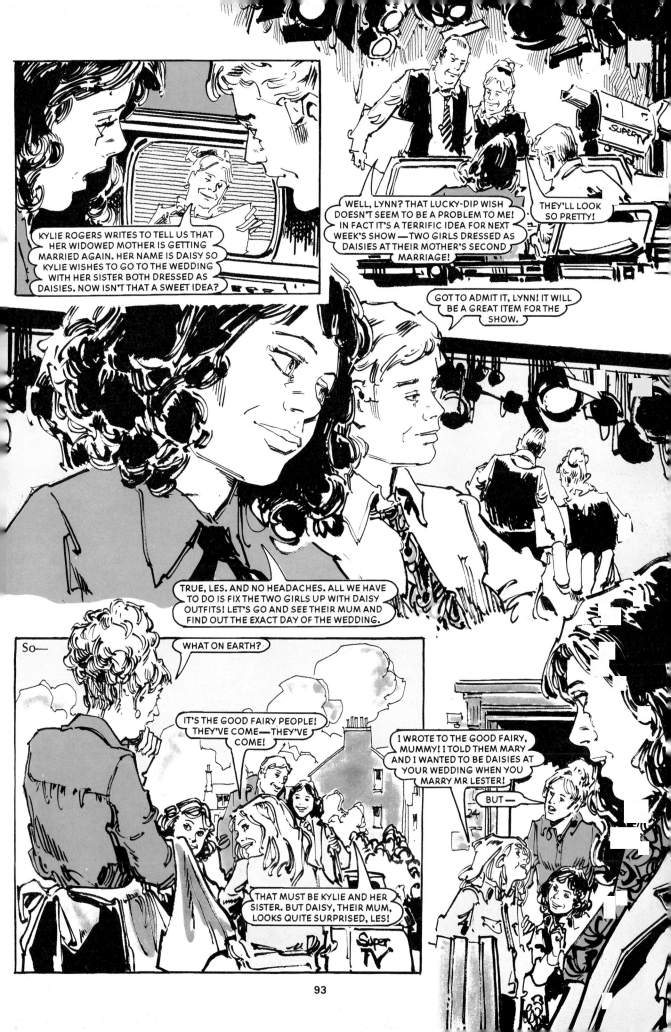

KYLIE ROGERS WRITES TO TELL US THAT HER WIDOWED MOTHER IS GETTING MARRIED AGAIN. HER NAME IS DAISY SO KYLIE WISHES TO GO TO THE WEDDING WITH HER SISTER BOTH DRESSED AS DAISIES. NOW ISN'T THAT A SWEET IDEA?

WELL, LYNN? THAT LUCKY-DIP WISH DOESN'T SEEM TO BE A PROBLEM TO ME! IN FACT IT'S A TERRIFIC IDEA FOR NEXT WEEK'S SHOW — TWO GIRLS DRESSED AS DAISIES AT THEIR MOTHER'S SECOND MARRIAGE!

THEY'LL LOOK SO PRETTY!

GOT TO ADMIT IT, LYNN! IT WILL BE A GREAT ITEM FOR THE SHOW.

TRUE, LES. AND NO HEADACHES. ALL WE HAVE TO DO IS FIX THE TWO GIRLS UP WITH DAISY OUTFITS! LET'S GO AND SEE THEIR MUM AND FIND OUT THE EXACT DAY OF THE WEDDING.

So—

WHAT ON EARTH?

IT'S THE GOOD FAIRY PEOPLE! THEY'VE COME — THEY'VE COME!

I WROTE TO THE GOOD FAIRY, MUMMY! I TOLD THEM MARY AND I WANTED TO BE DAISIES AT YOUR WEDDING WHEN YOU MARRY MR LESTER!

BUT—

THAT MUST BE KYLIE AND HER SISTER. BUT DAISY, THEIR MUM, LOOKS QUITE SURPRISED, LES!

And so, some time later—

DAISY AND ME ARE BOTH VERY MUCH IN LOVE, BUT I JUST CAN'T AFFORD TO GIVE HER THE KIND OF WEDDING SHE DESERVES. MY CYCLE BUSINESS ISN'T DOING TOO WELL.

IT COULD TAKE AGES FOR THE BUSINESS TO PICK UP! THERE MUST BE ANOTHER SOLUTION.

IT WAS A SWEET IDEA OF THE KIDS'—DRESSING-UP AS DAISIES FOR THE WEDDING, BUT—

WAIT A MINUTE! DAISIES—THAT TANDEM. IT MIGHT JUST WORK!

I'VE A TERRIFIC IDEA THAT MIGHT HELP YOU TO DO BOTH, BUT YOU'LL HAVE TO GO AHEAD AND GET MARRIED THIS WEEK. I'M SURE YOU'LL GET A SPECIAL LICENCE. NOW LISTEN CAREFULLY.

LISTEN, MR LESTER. YOU WANT TO GET MARRIED AND SOON, RIGHT? AND YOU'D LIKE TO HANG ON TO YOUR CYCLE BUSINESS TOO.

WELL, YES, OF COURSE, BUT—

I HOPE LYNN KNOWS WHAT SHE'S DOING!

So, on the day of the wedding—

AUNT JEMIMA IS ALL READY FOR WHEN THE CEREMONY IS OVER, LYNN.

GREAT! O.K, KYLIE! YOU AND YOUR SISTER ARE ALL SET. IN YOU GO FOR THE WEDDING! WE'LL ALL BE WAITING FOR YOU WHEN YOU COME OUT!

EXCITING, ISN'T IT, SIS? I KNEW THE GOOD FAIRY WOULDN'T LET US DOWN!

After the ceremony—

O.K, AUNT JEMIMA! NOW!

REGISTRAR

The K.O. Kids!

ONE morning, in Wansdale town —

PATTI

DEEPA

RITA

GLADYS

COMING SOON

IT'S A KNOCK-OUT!

WANSDALE V WALEFORD

THRILLS, SPILLS and FUN!

LOOK AT THIS, GIRLS! I EXPECT THE WANSDALE TEAM HAS ALREADY BEEN CHOSEN.

WHO CARES? I WOULDN'T GO IN FOR IT, IF THEY PLEADED WITH ME!

NOR WOULD I!

THEY DO SUCH DAFT STUNTS!

97

G

At Wansdale School —

I EXPECT YOU'VE SEEN THE POSTERS THAT HAVE BEEN GOING UP ALL OVER TOWN. OUR SCHOOL HAS BEEN ASKED TO ENTER FOUR COMPETITORS. SO I'M ASKING FOR VOLUNTEERS —

I'LL VOLUNTEER, MISS!

AND ME!

ME, TOO!

I'LL HAVE A GO!

YOU SAID YOU DIDN'T WANT TO GO IN FOR IT, RITA!

WHAT IF I DID? I CAN CHANGE MY MIND, CAN'T I?

THAT WAS WHEN WE THOUGHT WE DIDN'T HAVE A CHANCE!

Two days later —

WE'RE IN! ALL FOUR OF US!

THE IT'S A KNOCKOUT TEAM

TERRIFIC!

Then the training began —

THERE'S BOYS IN THE TEAM TOO, PATTI!

SO IT'LL BE FOUR GIRLS AND FOUR BOYS IN THE TEAM!

98

SHOW-OFF!

DON'T WATCH! DON'T ENCOURAGE HIM.

BET *YOU* CAN'T DO A HANDSTAND!

YEAH, YOU'VE GOT TO BE FIT TO BE ANY GOOD IN THE KNOCK-OUT COMPETITION!

IS THAT SO?

FANCY A GO ON THE TRAMPOLINE?

NICE LOOKING, ISN'T HE?

I HATE NICE LOOKING BOYS! THEY THINK THEY'RE SO WONDERFUL!

GET ON! SHOW US WHAT YOU CAN DO!

WE'LL STAND BY TO CATCH YOU IF YOU FALL!

I'LL SHOW 'EM, PATTI.

ALL YOU HAVE TO DO IS BOUNCE UP AND DOWN!

WHY DOES RITA HAVE TO TAKE UP EVERY CHALLENGE? SHE'LL ONLY MAKE HERSELF LOOK SILLY!

GO A BIT HIGHER!

YOU MEAN LIKE THIS —?

AND THIS?

SIMPLE, ISN'T IT!

THAT WAS A SURPRISE, RITA! YOU WERE REALLY GOOD!

I USED TO DO A LOT OF IT AT THE LAST SCHOOL I WENT TO! IT LET THEM KNOW WE'RE NOT COMPLETE WALLIES, ANYWAY!

Meanwhile, in another part of the playing fields —

YOU'LL HAVE TO CLIMB UP ONE OF THESE THINGS DURING THE COMPETITION, SO YOU'D BETTER GET USED TO IT!

I'LL NEVER BE ABLE TO CLIMB THAT!

DON'T BE SILLY, GLADYS! YOU CAN DO IT!

COME ON, GLAD!

I CAN'T! I'M FRIGHTENED OF HEIGHTS!

YOU'RE HARDLY OFF THE GROUND, GIRL!

100

Gladys got up and over eventually —

PHEW! I'M EXHAUSTED!

YOU'LL GET USED TO IT AND REMEMBER IT'S ONLY FUN, GIRLS! YOU WON'T ENTER EVERY EVENT IN THE COMPETITION, ANYWAY. I'LL SORT OUT WHICH ONES YOU'RE BEST AT.

THERE'S STILL A WEEK TO GO! BY THE TIME THE COMPETITION STARTS, YOU'LL BE AS FIT AS A FIDDLE.

A few days later —

HOW'S THE TRAINING GOING, RITA?

IT HASN'T! I'M TAKING IT EASY! BEING IN THE KNOCK-OUT COMP'S ALL RIGHT, BUT I'M NOT MAKING IT MY LIFE'S WORK!

BUT IF WE WIN, WE GO INTO THE NEXT ROUND! THEN ON UNTIL WE REACH THE FINAL IN PARIS!

PARIS? I DIDN'T KNOW THAT! MAYBE IT IS WORTH A BIT OF EFFORT! I COULD BUY SOME CLOTHES IN PARIS!

Gladys Bates was worried. Next morning —

WHERE ON EARTH ARE YOU GOING IN THE RAIN, GLADYS?

I'M GOING JOGGING, MUM! NOT MANY DAYS LEFT NOW!

I MUST BE MAD! I'M ONLY DOING THIS BECAUSE I DON'T WANT TO LET THE OTHERS DOWN. BUT I'LL NEVER WIN ANYTHING — I'M NOT GOOD ENOUGH!

102

Then all of a sudden —

IT'S GLADYS!

SHE'S REALLY RACING!

I'M GLAD I DID MY JOGGING IN MUDDY LANES!

GLADYS IS FIRST! TEN POINTS FOR WANSDALE!

Patti was in the next game —

NOW THE SLIPPERY POLE! FIRST ONE ACROSS WINS!

THEY'RE ALL OFF!

PATTI HASN'T STARTED, YET!

IT'S NO USE TRYING TO WALK ALONG THE POLE —

THIS IS THE ONLY WAY TO DO IT!

YOU'RE NEXT, RITA! ME AND PATTI HAVE BOTH WON!

WHAT GREAT FEAT ARE YOU GOING TO DO?

SOMETHING STYLISH — ON THE TRAMPOLINE!

I'M NOT GOING TO LOOK A FOOL LIKE YOU LOT!

AND NOW WANSDALE BATTLE AGAINST WALEFORD — IN THE GREAT BOUNCING CONTEST! ALL THEY HAVE TO DO — IS POP A FEW BALLOONS AT THE SAME TIME —

— DRESSED AS CHICKENS!

SHE DIDN'T SAY ANYTHING ABOUT BEING TOGGED UP LIKE THAT!

I DON'T THINK SHE KNEW!

THEY'LL NEVER DO IT!

WHICH ONE'S RITA?

I DUNNO!

THIS IS SO EMBARRASSING! THE SOONER I GET IT OVER, THE BETTER!

And—

POP!

POP!

THAT'S RITA! SHE'S WINNING!

ANOTHER TEN POINTS FOR WANSDALE!

IT'S THE FINAL GAME. THE BIG BALL ROLL!

WE'RE ALL IN THIS! IT'LL BE A LAUGH!

WELL I REFUSE TO DRESS UP IN A SILLY OUTFIT FOR THAT!

IT'S A CLOSE CONTEST! WHICHEVER TEAM WINS THIS GAME IS THE WINNER OF THE WHOLE COMPETITION, AND THEN GO INTO THE NEXT ROUND!

PUSH!

OW! GET IT OFF ME!

POOR OLD RITA! SHE'S REALLY GOING THROUGH IT TODAY!

107

Dear Katy...

'DEAR KATY, SINCE LAST I WRITE, THE RAIN IT FALLS IN HEAVINESS.' I LOVE IT WHEN SOLANGE GETS HER ENGLISH MIXED UP! MIND YOU, I BET MY FRENCH IS EVEN FUNNIER TO HER!

HERE'S A PHOTO OF SOLANGE AND HER BOYFRIEND, HENRI. IMAGINE SOLANGE HAVING A BOYFRIEND AT HER AGE. MY MUM WOULD HAVE A FIT!

And next month —

'HENRI AND I MET CLAUDE AT THE CAFE AND WENT ON TO A PARTY . . .' SOLANGE ALWAYS HAS SO MUCH FUN — SHE MUST THINK I'M REALLY BORING!

MY LIFE'S A REAL DRAG COMPARED TO SOLANGE'S! I BET SHE SPENDS ALL WEEKEND AT THAT CAFE WITH HER MATES, WHILE ALL I HAVE TO LOOK FORWARD TO IS WINDOW-SHOPPING WITH ROZ!

On Saturday—

MY FEET ACHE, ROZ. LET'S GO IN THERE FOR A DRINK AND A SIT DOWN.

NOT THAT PLACE! IT'S WHERE PHIL DASHWOOD AND THOSE OTHER FOURTH YEAR LAYABOUTS HANG OUT. LET'S GO TO DELL'S.

But Katy persuaded Roz—

SEE, IT'S NOT SO BAD AND NOBODY'S GOING TO EAT YOU.

ONLY FUDDY-DUDDYS GO TO DELL'S. SOLANGE WOULDN'T BE SEEN DEAD IN THERE AND NEITHER WOULD I.

WE HAVEN'T SEEN YOU TWO IN HERE BEFORE. MOVE UP, AND WE CAN ALL GET FRIENDLY.

I KNEW THIS WAS A MISTAKE. COME ON, KATY, LET'S GO.

DON'T BE A SPOILSPORT. I'M STAYING.

THAT'S MY GIRL! SHE CAN TREAT US ALL TO A COKE, CAN'T SHE, LADS?

So Roz left without Katy —

KEEP THE NOISE DOWN, YOU BOYS, OR YOU CAN GET OUT.

I FEEL SCARED — BUT IT'S FUN TOO. NOW I'LL REALLY HAVE SOMETHING TO WRITE AND TELL SOLANGE!

On Monday—

HI, GORGEOUS!

I SUPPOSE YOU'LL BE JOINING YOUR NEW FRIENDS!

ROZ IS JUST JEALOUS! I HADN'T REALISED HOW DULL MY FRIENDS WERE UNTIL I MET PHIL AND HIS CROWD. NOW I'M HAVING FUN — JUST LIKE SOLANGE.

SEE YOU DOWN THE CAFE TONIGHT?

SURE.

I'VE LOADS OF HOMEWORK, BUT IT'LL HAVE TO WAIT. I'LL JUST TELL MUM I'M GOING TO ROZ'S.

That night —

HEY, LADS, HERE'S KATY. IT'LL BE CRISPS ALL ROUND — HER TREAT!

ALL I'VE GOT IS MY SCHOOL LUNCH MONEY, BUT THEY'LL LIKE ME BETTER IF I TREAT THEM.

An hour later—

I THOUGHT I'D FIND YOU HERE. I CAME TO WARN YOU THAT YOUR MUM'S ON THE WARPATH. SHE PHONED MY PLACE TO SEE IF I KNEW WHERE YOU'D GOT TO.

I SUPPOSE YOU ENJOYED TELLING HER!

OF COURSE I DIDN'T TELL HER — BUT I THOUGHT YOU'D WANT TO GO HOME!

LEAVE KATY ALONE! SHE'S JUST HAVING FUN WITH HER MATES.

But—

I SHOULD HAVE GONE WITH ROZ. IT'S — IT'S GETTING BEYOND A JOKE HERE. I'M SURE THERE'S GOING TO BE TROUBLE. THEY'RE REALLY ROWDY.

Later —

OI! YOU HAVEN'T PAID FOR THOSE LAST CANS OF DRINKS . . .

YOU'LL HAVE TO CATCH US FIRST, GRANDAD!

OH — MIND THAT LADY, PHIL . . .

OUT OF THE WAY, SILLY OLD BAT!

SHE'S HURT!

SHE'LL BE ALL RIGHT. COME ON, JUST LEAVE HER!

But Katy couldn't leave her —

I WAS WAITING FOR YOU OVER THE ROAD AND SAW IT ALL. THE CAFE OWNER'S CALLED THE POLICE AND AN AMBULANCE.

HOW COULD THEY JUST RUN OFF? SHE LOOKS BADLY HURT.

SHE WAS ONE OF 'EM. THE OTHERS SCARPERED.

LOOKS LIKE YOU'RE IN TROUBLE, KID. YOU'VE GOT SOME EXPLAINING TO DO.

KATY WASN'T REALLY IN WITH THAT GANG, TRULY! SHE JUST HAPPENED TO BE IN THE CAFE WHEN THE TROUBLE BLEW UP!

ALL RIGHT, I'LL LET YOU OFF THIS TIME. THE OWNER TELLS ME YOU'RE NOT USUALLY WITH THESE BOYS — BUT ANY MORE TROUBLE AND I'LL BE ROUND TO SEE YOUR PARENTS.

THANKS FOR STICKING BY ME, ROZ.

THAT'S WHAT REAL MATES ARE FOR!

SOLANGE'S LETTERS ARE STILL FULL OF WHAT SHE GETS UP TO BUT IT DOESN'T SOUND SO WONDERFUL NOW. I ONLY HOPE IT DOESN'T END IN TROUBLE FOR HER, THE WAY IT NEARLY DID FOR ME!

Brassribs

CINDY ROGERS had been marooned on a desert island in the Pacific. But she wasn't alone. With her was Brassribs, a robot butler invented by her Dad!

YES! JUST AS I SUSPECTED. THEY ARE OF THE MELEAGRIS GALLOPAVO FAMILY, AND JUST WHAT I NEED. THIS WILL BE A TIMELY SURPRISE FOR MISS CINDY!

But it was Brassribs who had the surprise. Suddenly—

OH, NO! BRASSRIBS! HELP!

MISS CINDY'S VOICE! AND SHE APPEARS TO BE IN TROUBLE. I —

In his alarm, Brassribs slipped from the branch and—

OOOF! MY MEMORY BANKS RECALL THE SAYING — MORE HASTE, LESS SPEED!

BUT, HASTE IS WHAT I NEED IF MISS CINDY IS IN TROUBLE!

Moments later—

MISS CINDY! ARE YOU ALL RIGHT?

NO! MY CALENDAR! I'VE BEEN KEEPING IT SO CAREFULLY, MARKING OFF THE DAYS IN CHARCOAL — AND NOW THAT RAIN LAST NIGHT HAS WASHED IT ALL OFF!

IS THAT ALL THAT'S WRONG, MISS?

ALL? IT'S DISASTROUS, BRASSRIBS. NOW I DON'T KNOW HOW MANY DAYS WE'VE BEEN HERE!

IF THE DATE IS ALL YOU REQUIRE, MISS, WHY DIDN'T YOU ASK? IT IS NOW THE TWENTY-THIRD OF DECEMBER.

OH, NO! IT — IT'S ALMOST CHRISTMAS! NOW I FEEL REALLY MISERABLE, BRASSRIBS.

CHRISTMAS! AND WITHOUT DADDY — AND NO GUESTS, NO GAMES, NO CHRISTMAS DINNER — NOTHING!

BUT YOU HAVE ME, MISS CINDY, AND I SHALL DO MY BEST TO MAKE IT AS PLEASANT AND CHEERFUL A CHRISTMAS AS IS IN MY POWER. PLEASE CHEER-UP.

NOW, MISS. I HAVE THINGS TO DO. I SUGGEST YOU MAKE YOURSELF BUSY, FOR OCCUPYING ONES MIND IS THE BEST THING TO STOP ONE FEELING SORRY FOR ONESELF!

YOU'RE RIGHT AS USUAL, BRASSRIBS! AND THERE *IS* PLENTY TO DO.

I SHALL ABONDON PURSUIT OF THE MELEAGRIS GALLOPAVO, FOR THE MOMENT, AND FETCH SOME CANVAS!

But, a little later—

OH, NO! BRASSRIBS! HELP!

MISS CINDY!

HER VOICE CAME FROM THIS DIRECTION! THAT ROCK-FACE LOOKS AS IF IT HAS JUST COLLAPSED!

MISS CINDY!

IF MISS CINDY IS BENEATH THIS ROCK I HAVE ONLY SECONDS TO SAVE HER!

Then—

WHAT ARE YOU DOING, BRASSRIBS? THERE MUST BE SOMETHING VERY IMPORTANT UNDER THAT LOT!

MISS CINDY!

I HEARD YOUR CRY FOR HELP. I ASSUMED YOU WERE UNDER THIS FALLEN ROCK.

YOU'RE HEARING THINGS, BRASSRIBS! MAYBE YOU'RE REPLAYING YOUR MEMORY-TAPES WITHOUT KNOWING IT!

Back at the camp—

HEY! ALL THE FRUIT HAS GONE! THAT'S ODD.

OR COULD IT BE THAT YOUR MEMORY-TAPES ARE FAULTY, MISS CINDY! PERHAPS YOU ATE IT ALL AND FORGOT.

Later, after a fruit-picking session—

IF I DIDN'T KNOW BETTER, I'D SAY YOU WERE CROSS, BRASSRIBS! THAT SOUNDED VERY LIKE SARCASM TO ME!

I AM INCAPABLE OF SUCH HUMAN EMOTION, MISS. BUT I HAVE THINGS TO DO. I SUGGEST YOU PICK SOME MORE FRUIT!

MISS CINDY!

THAT'S BRASSRIBS! IT SOUNDS URGENT. IF HE'S CALLING ME FOR HELP IT MUST BE SERIOUS!

NO SIGN OF HIM. BUT I'M CERTAIN HIS VOICE CAME FROM SOMEWHERE AROUND HERE!

EEEK! OH, NO! IT'S A BOG!

I-I CAN'T GET A HOLD! I'M SINKING!

116

Meanwhile—

BRASSRIBS! HELP ME!

MISS CINDY'S VOICE. OR IS IT? PERHAPS SHE WAS RIGHT. IT COULD BE A MECHANICAL FAULT.

While Brassribs checked over his system—

BRASSRIBS! HELP!

WHERE IS HE? HE — HE'S NEVER BEEN SO SLOW BEFORE! I'M SINKING DEEPER BY THE SECOND!

BRASSRIBS! HELP!

NO! THAT WAS MISS CINDY'S VOICE. I'M SURE OF IT.

He arrived just in time!

OH, BRASSRIBS! AT LAST!

YOU ARE SAFE NOW, MISS CINDY! YOU'LL BE OUT IN MOMENTS!

WHAT TOOK YOU SO LONG, BRASSRIBS? I'D ALMOST GIVEN UP!

I MUST APOLOGISE, MISS. I DOUBTED WHAT I HEARD AFTER YOUR SUGGESTION THAT I WAS MECHANICALLY AT FAULT! THE LAST TIME I HEARD YOU CALL —

— IT PROVED TO BE A MISTAKE. YOU HADN'T CALLED AT ALL!

RIGHT! AND I GOT INTO THIS PICKLE BECAUSE I THOUGHT YOU HAD CALLED OUT TO ME! WHAT'S GOING ON HERE, BRASSRIBS?

When they got back to the camp—

I'LL JUST TAKE A SHOWER, AND THEN — HEY!

LOOK! THE FRUIT-BOWL — IT'S EMPTY AGAIN!

ARE YOU CERTAIN THAT YOU FILLED IT, MISS?

OF COURSE I FILLED IT! I WAS JUST PUTTING THE FRUIT INTO THE BOWL WHEN I HEARD YOU CALL FOR HELP.

BUT I DIDN'T CALL FOR HELP, MISS CINDY!

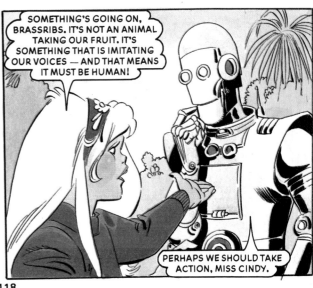

SOMETHING'S GOING ON, BRASSRIBS. IT'S NOT AN ANIMAL TAKING OUR FRUIT. IT'S SOMETHING THAT IS IMITATING OUR VOICES — AND THAT MEANS IT MUST BE HUMAN!

PERHAPS WE SHOULD TAKE ACTION, MISS CINDY.

118

WE SHOULD BEHAVE NORMALLY. YOU PICK SOME MORE FRUIT AND REFILL THE BOWL. THEN WE SHALL HIDE IN THE JUNGLE AND WATCH TO SEE WHAT OCCURS.

GOOD IDEA, BRASSRIBS.

Later—

RIGHT! BRASSRIBS IS WAITING FOR ME UNDER COVER. I MUST TRY TO BEHAVE NORMALLY, BUT I CAN'T HELP FEELING JUMPY.

OH, NO! BRASSRIBS! HELP!

THAT IS YOUR VOICE, MISS CINDY!

THAT'S MY VOICE ALL RIGHT, BRASSRIBS! WHOEVER IT IS, IS A GREAT MIMIC!

Quietly, they crept out of cover, and—

I DON'T BELIEVE IT! CHIMPS!

AMAZING, MISS CINDY! I HAVE NEVER YET KNOWN OF A CHIMPANZEE THAT COULD IMITATE A HUMAN VOICE!

But then—

MISS CINDY! MISS CINDY!

NO, BRASSRIBS! THERE'S THE MIMIC! IT'S THAT BIRD!

MY MEMORY-BANKS TELL ME IT IS OF THE GRACULA RELIGIOSA FAMILY!

119

WHAT FAMILY?

YOU PROBABLY KNOW IT BETTER AS THE MYNAH BIRD, MISS CINDY. ONE OF THE MOST REMARKABLE MIMICS. BUT HOW THE CHIMPANZEES GOT HERE, I CANNOT EXPLAIN!

WHO CARES, BRASSRIBS! THEY MAY SOLVE ONE OF OUR CHRISTMAS PROBLEMS — LACK OF GUESTS!

GOOD IDEA, MISS CINDY!

On Christmas Day—

BRASSRIBS! HOW DO YOU MANAGE THESE THINGS? A REAL ROAST TURKEY — AND YOU'RE DRESSED AS SANTA WITH A SACK! YOU'RE A MARVEL!

I SAW SOME TURKEYS IN THE JUNGLE AND THE SANTA SUIT I MADE FROM CANVAS, DYED WITH BERRIES.

MERRY CHRISTMAS! MERRY CHRISTMAS, EVERYONE!

AND I TAUGHT THE BIRD A SUITABLE SENTIMENT, MISS CINDY!

BRASSRIBS! WHAT WOULD I DO WITHOUT YOU? MERRY CHRISTMAS TO YOU, TOO!

JASON
DONOVAN

SEAL ROCK PRODUCTIONS 1989

JANUARY

S	—	6	13	20	27
M	—	7	14	21	28
Tu	1	8	15	22	29
W	2	9	16	23	30
Th	3	10	17	24	31
F	4	11	18	25	—
S	5	12	19	26	—

FEBRUARY

S	—	3	10	17	24
M	—	4	11	18	25
Tu	—	5	12	19	26
W	—	6	13	20	27
Th	—	7	14	21	28
F	1	8	15	22	—
S	2	9	16	23	—

MARCH

S	3	10	17	24	31
M	4	11	18	25	—
Tu	5	12	19	26	—
W	6	13	20	27	—
Th	7	14	21	28	—
F	1	8	15	22	29	—
S	2	9	16	23	30	—

BUNTY ANNUAL CALENDAR - 1991

PET SHOP BOYS

APRIL						MAY						JUNE					
S	—	7	14	21	28	S	—	5	12	19	26	S	2	9	16	23	30
M	1	8	15	22	29	M	—	6	13	20	27	M	3	10	17	24	—
Tu	2	9	16	23	30	Tu	—	7	14	21	28	Tu	4	11	18	25	—
W	3	10	17	24	—	W	1	8	15	22	29	W	5	12	19	26	—
Th	4	11	18	25	—	Th	2	9	16	23	30	Th	6	13	20	27	—
F	5	12	19	26	—	F	3	10	17	24	31	F	7	14	21	28	—
S	6	13	20	27	—	S	4	11	18	25	—	S	1	8	15	22	29	—

BUNTY ANNUAL CALENDAR - 1991

RALPH MACCHIO

JULY							AUGUST							SEPTEMBER					
S	—	7	14	21	28		S	—	4	11	18	25		S	1	8	15	22	29
M	1	8	15	22	29		M	—	5	12	19	26		M	2	9	16	23	30
Tu	2	9	16	23	30		Tu	—	6	13	20	27		Tu	3	10	17	24	—
W	3	10	17	24	31		W	—	7	14	21	28		W	4	11	18	25	—
Th	4	11	18	25	—		Th	1	8	15	22	29		Th	5	12	19	26	—
F	5	12	19	26	—		F	2	9	16	23	30		F	6	13	20	27	—
S	6	13	20	27	—		S	3	10	17	24	31		S	7	14	21	28	—

BUNTY ANNUAL CALENDAR - 1991

BIG FUN

OCTOBER						
S	—	6	13	20	27	
M	—	7	14	21	28	
Tu	1	8	15	22	29	
W	2	9	16	23	30	
Th	3	10	17	24	31	
F	4	11	18	25	—	
S	5	12	19	26	—	

NOVEMBER						
S	—	3	10	17	24	
M	—	4	11	18	25	
Tu	—	5	12	19	26	
W	—	6	13	20	27	
Th	—	7	14	21	28	
F	1	8	15	22	29	
S	2	9	16	23	30	

DECEMBER						
S	1	8	15	22	29	
M	2	9	16	23	30	
Tu	3	10	17	24	31	
W	4	11	18	25	—	
Th	5	12	19	26	—	
F	6	13	20	27	—	
S	7	14	21	28	—	

WHY SO GLUM, GUYS? IT'S THE SCHOOL CHRISTMAS DISCO TONIGHT.

Bunty
A GIRL LIKE YOU

YEAH, BUT THERE'S ALSO A LIVE BROS CONCERT ON T.V.

AND WE CAN'T BE IN TWO PLACES AT ONCE.

THAT'S NO PROBLEM. I'LL VIDEO IT AND YOU CAN COME ROUND TO MY HOUSE TOMORROW TO WATCH IT.

THAT'S ACE, BUNTY!

NOW YOU WON'T FORGET, DAD? BROS CONCERT — 8 O'CLOCK.

DON'T WORRY, BUNTY. ENJOY THE DISCO.

THIS IS A GREAT DISCO.

EVEN BETTER, KNOWING WE'RE NOT MISSING THE BROS CONCERT.

Next evening —

THIS IS IT!

GREAT.

FOOTBALL? DAD!

HA-HA! BET THAT GAVE YOU A FRIGHT! THIS IS WHAT YOU'RE LOOKING FOR!

THIS IS GREAT! GOOD OLD DAD.